# *Jumanji*

## TODD STRASSER

Level 2

Retold by John Escott
Series Editors: Andy Hopkins and Jocelyn Potter

**Pearson Education Limited**
Edinburgh Gate, Harlow,
Essex CM20 2JE, England
and Associated Companies throughout the world.

ISBN 0 582 41663 9

First published by Puffin Books 1996
This adaptation first published by Penguin Books 1997
Published by Addison Wesley Longman Limited and Penguin Books Ltd. 1998
New edition first published 1999

5  7  9  10  8  6

Text copyright © John Escott 1997
Photography copyright © TriStar Pictures Inc. 1996
All rights reserved

The moral right of the adapter has been asserted

Set in 11/14pt Monotype Bembo by
Rowland Phototypesetting Ltd,
Bury St Edmunds, Suffolk
Printed in Spain by Mateu Cromo, S.A. Pinto (Madrid)

Published by Pearson Education Limited in association with
Penguin Books Ltd., both companies being subsidiaries of Pearson Plc

the titles available in the Penguin Readers series please write to your local
on office or to: Marketing Department, Penguin Longman Publishing,
80 Strand, London, WC2R 0RL

# Contents

# Introduction

*It was evening when he opened it, on the dining room table. His mother and father were upstairs. The box opened into a game board, with tokens and dice. On the board, four different 'roads' went to a small glass 'eye' in the centre.* Jumanji, *he read from the box.* Do you want to leave the world behind? Then this game is for you.

In the year 1869, in a small town in New England, USA, two young brothers bury a dangerous game called 'Jumanji' in a hole under some trees. The boys are afraid. 'Somebody could find it,' says the younger boy. 'Then God help them!' says his brother.

Somebody *does* find the game – a hundred years later! And with the first throw of the dice, something unusual happens. But this is only the beginning . . .

Twenty-six years later, somebody must finish that game! And when two children – Peter and Judy – find the Jumanji box, strange things start to happen again.

Can they finish the game before it finishes them? First they must face lions, crocodiles, and a hunter with a gun!

The story Jumanji began life as a book by Chris Van Allsburg, in 1981. Then it was a film. Robin Williams was the star and many people saw and loved it. Then Todd Strasser wrote a book from the film.

Chris Van Allsberg was born in 1949 in Michigan, USA. In 1979 he wrote his first children's book, *The Garden of Abdul Gasazi*. He then wrote more books – all for children. He also makes the pictures for all his books – these are very important to his stories.

## *Some Words from the Story*

Before you read this story, you must know the words for all the things in the picture on this page. Use a dictionary. Find the right numbers on the picture for the words below and write the numbers and words together, e.g. *1 jungle*

| | | | |
|---|---|---|---|
| board-game | vine | glass 'eye' | tokens |
| mosquito | jungle | hunter | monkey |
| rhinoceros | tail | crocodile | handcuffs |
| dice | pelican | spider | lion |
| bat | elephant | zebra | |

# Brantford, New Hampshire, 1869

It was a dark night and the wind made a noise in the trees. The two young brothers made a hole, then threw a big box into it. Suddenly, the younger boy fell into the hole.

'Help!' he shouted. A noise came from inside the box. *Brummm-tum-tum. Brummm-tum-tum* . . . 'It's coming after me!' But the older brother put his arm into the hole and pulled the younger boy out.

'Run! Run!' said the younger boy.

'No!' said his brother. 'We must bury it!'

They buried the box under the trees.

'Somebody could find it,' said the younger boy.

'Then God help them!' said his brother.


# Chapter 1   Brantford, New Hampshire, 1969

It was a September afternoon, and twelve-year-old Alan Parrish moved along the street on his bicycle.

'*Get ready to die, Parrish!*' somebody shouted.

He turned and saw Billy Jessup with some other boys.

There was a factory building in front of Alan. It said, PARRISH SHOES – THE BEST SHOES IN NEW ENGLAND! on the outside of it. He quickly jumped off his bike and ran inside.

'Go on!' shouted Billy. 'Run to Daddy! We can wait!'

Alan ran into a big room. He heard the machines, and walked between the lines of men at their work tables. Carl Bentley, a twenty-year-old black man, looked up and smiled.

'Hello, Carl,' said Alan. It was good to see a friendly face.

*'What is it?' said Alan.*
*'It's a new sports shoe,' said Carl. 'In a year or two*
*they're going to be in every home in America.'*

'I want to show you something I've made,' said Carl. 'I'm going to show it to your father this afternoon.' He took a shoe from under his work table and gave it to Alan.

'What is it?' said Alan.

'It's a new sports shoe,' said Carl. 'In a year or two they're going to be in every home in America.'

Alan saw his father coming. He put Carl's sports shoe down on a machine and went across to Mr Parrish.

'What are you doing here?' Sam Parrish asked his son.

'Can – can you take me home in the car?' asked Alan.

Mr Parrish looked at him carefully. 'Billy Jessup again?' he said. 'You mustn't run away from something because you're afraid of it, Alan. Now, go away, son.'

Alan started to walk back to the stairs. Suddenly, there was a noise from one of the machines. It began to jump about, and smoke came out of it. Alan watched his father pull something out of the machine. It was Carl's new sports shoe!

'Who did this?' shouted Mr Parrish, angrily.

Alan wanted to tell his father that he put Carl's sports shoe on the machine, but he didn't want his father to shout at him.

He ran out of the factory and into the road with his bike.

Billy and his friends came out from behind the trees. Alan looked around quickly, but Billy Jessup moved across to him.

'I'm going to stop you talking to my girlfriend,' he said.

Alan looked surprised. 'Sarah? But –'

They jumped on him and all five boys hit and kicked Alan. Then they ran away, and took his bike with them.

Alan got up and tried not to cry.

*Brummm-tum-tum. Brummm-tum-tum . . .*

'What's that?' He looked around. 'Builders are making new offices near the factory. Did the noise come from there?'

The men stopped work to go and get their coffee.

*Brummm-tum-tum. Brummm-tum-tum.* Alan went to look. The noise came from a half-buried box in a hole. It was a big box, and it took Alan two or three minutes to get it out and open it. Inside was a box with pictures of jungle animals and a hunter on the outside of it. And the word: JUMANJI.

Alan started to open the box, but the men began to come back. He quickly put it under his arm, and walked home.

*It took Alan two or three minutes to get it out and open it.*
*Inside was a box with pictures of jungle animals and a hunter*
*on the outside of it. And the word: JUMANJI*

## Chapter 2   The Game Starts

It was evening when he opened it, on the dining table. His mother and father were upstairs. The box opened into a game board, with tokens and dice. On the board, four different 'roads' went to a small glass 'eye' in the center.

Then Alan heard his mother and father outside the room. He quickly shut the box and put it under his chair.

'I've told your father that there were four more boys with Billy Jessup,' said Mrs Parrish, when she came in.

'I didn't know that, Alan,' said Mr Parrish. He smiled and

gave Alan a photograph of a school. 'We think you're ready to go to Cliffside School. You're a man now. You showed us that when you didn't run away from Billy Jessup today.'

Alan looked at the photograph. The boys at Cliffside School only came home in the holidays. 'You – you don't want me to live here!' he said to his mother and father.

'Parrish men always go to Cliffside,' said his father. 'I did.'

'Perhaps I don't want to be you!' shouted Alan. 'Perhaps I don't want to be a Parrish man, or go to Cliffside School!'

Mr Parrish began to get angry. 'We're going there next Sunday, Alan,' he said. 'I don't want to hear another word about it. Now, your mother and I are going out to dinner.'

'Good!' shouted Alan. 'I'm never going to talk to you again!'

When he heard the front door shut, he ran up to his room.

'I'm getting out of this town,' he thought. 'The next place I go to, nobody will *know* the name Parrish!' He put some clothes, food and the Jumanji game into a bag. Then he walked to the front door. But there was somebody outside.

It was Sarah Whittle – a pretty thirteen-year-old girl. And behind her was Alan's bicycle. She looked at Alan's bag.

'Where are you going?' she asked.

He liked Sarah very much, but he was too angry to answer.

'I told Billy to give me your bike,' said Sarah.

'Good. Thanks.' He didn't look at her.

'Alan, I wanted to help you,' she said.

'Go and help your boyfriend,' said Alan, angrily.

'Billy's *not* my boyfriend.' *Brummm-tum-tum* . . . The noise came from inside his bag. 'What's that?' she asked.

Alan wanted to go, but he wanted to show her the game, too. A minute later they were inside the house, and he put

'These things can fly at you at night, run quickly, do not try to fight.' *Suddenly a noise came from across the room. It was the noise of something flying!*

the bag on the floor and opened it. He took out the game.

*Jumanji,* he read from the box. *Do you want to leave the world behind? Then this game is for you. The first one to finish and shout Jumanji wins the game.*

Sarah looked at the dice in her hand and said, 'I don't play board-games.' Then she dropped them on to the board. One stopped at four, the other showed a two . . . *and one of the tokens moved to the sixth square on the board.*

'What – ?' began Sarah.

There were words in the glass eye in the center now. Alan read them. *These things can fly at you at night, run quickly, do not try to fight.*

Suddenly, a noise came from across the room. It was the noise of something flying!

'Quickly, put the board away!' said Sarah.

Without thinking, Alan dropped the dice on the board. They stopped at a two and a three. Now another token moved to the fifth square. More words came into the glass eye and Alan read them. *Go to the jungle now, and wait! Somebody must throw a five or eight.* 'What does –! Help! I'm getting smaller and smaller!' *And the board began to pull Alan into it, through the glass eye.*

Suddenly, hundreds of black bats flew out of the fire-place.

'*Alan!*' screamed Sarah. But Alan was inside the game!

Sarah ran – out of the room, and out of the house.


## Chapter 3    1995


Peter Shepherd and his twelve-year-old sister, Judy, stood outside the big house in Brantford, New Hampshire with their Aunt Nora. Their mother and father were dead – in a car accident in the Canadian Rocky Mountains.

Aunt Nora was thirty-two years old. She did not have a husband, and knew nothing about children.

'Come inside!' she said. Judy and Peter went inside the house.

'When did anybody last live here?' said Judy. Everything looked old – the tables, the chairs, everything.

Aunt Nora walked through the rooms. She smiled. She had plans for the house. She wanted to make it into a small hotel. 'The bar can go here,' she said, 'and the desk here.'

They brought in the bags and other things from the car. Then Aunt Nora took the children out to a restaurant for dinner. When they got back, it was time to go to bed.

*Peter Shepherd and his twelve-year-old sister, Judy*

Peter and Judy went to their new bedrooms. When he was in bed, Peter took a photograph out of a book on the table by his bed. It was a photograph of his mom and dad.

*Brummm-tum-tum. Brummm-tum-tum . . .*

What was that? He looked up above his head. A minute later, his bedroom door began to open, and he quickly put the photograph back in the book before Judy came in.

'Move over,' she said, and got into his bed. 'Did you hear something?' He didn't answer her question.

'I want Mom and Dad,' he said quietly.

*Brummm-tum-tum. Brummm-tum-tum . . .*

It was a long time before they went to sleep that night.

◆

The next day, at their new school, Peter and Judy learned all about Aunt Nora's new house.

'A twelve-year-old boy called Alan Parrish lived there,' a girl told them. 'He went away twenty-six years ago, and nobody ever saw him again. Some people say that his father cut him up and buried him all over the house.'

Peter and Judy tried not to think about this.

The next morning, Aunt Nora planned to leave early. After breakfast, she said, 'The school bus is coming in a minute. There's food in the refrigerator for later, and . . .'

*Brummm-tum-tum. Brummm-tum-tum . . .*

The sound came from upstairs. Peter and Judy looked at their aunt, but she didn't stop talking.

The noise stopped.

'You go on out,' Judy said. 'We're OK.'

'All right,' said Aunt Nora. 'Be good.' She turned and went out of the front door. Judy quickly shut it behind her.

She looked at Peter. 'You *do* hear it,' she said.

'Hear what?' asked Peter.

*Brummm-tum-tum. Brummm-tum-tum . . .*

Without a word, they ran upstairs. The noise came from the little room at the top of the house. But when they got there, it stopped. They looked around. The room had boxes and old pictures and things in it. *Brummm-tum-tum!*

It came from behind Judy. Peter ran across to a box with the word JUMANJI on the outside. Carefully, he opened up the game. Two tokens were on the board but Peter couldn't move them. Then he found two more, and the dice. The two tokens jumped out of his hand on to the first square!

Peter gave the dice to Judy. 'Y – you go first,' he said.

'OK,' said Judy, and she dropped the dice on to the board.

*Brummm-tum-tum! Brummm-tum-tum!*

9

Judy's token moved across the squares! Then they saw some words on the glass eye in the centre.

*Look out! These flying things can bite!* read Judy. *They come at you from left and right!*

Suddenly, they heard a noise – BZZZZZZ.

They turned around in time to see three mosquitoes as big as small birds! Judy quickly took off her shoe. She hit the first mosquito with it – and sent it crashing through the window. The other two turned and followed it outside.

Peter and Judy looked at the board. Peter took the dice.

'Don't!' shouted Judy.

But it was too late. He dropped them and they stopped at two number 1's. *Brummm-tum-tum! Brummm-tum-tum!*

New words came into the glass eye in the centre. *It has a long tail and lives in a tree. But is it dangerous? Wait and see!*

Crashing noises came from below. Judy ran out of the room, and Peter took the dice and followed her. They ran downstairs to the kitchen. They could hear breaking plates and strange screams. Judy pushed open the kitchen door.

Inside were twelve brown monkeys. Some threw plates and cups and food across the room. Others threw knives!

Judy quickly closed the door. 'We must have another look at the game,' she said.

When they were back in the room at the top of the house again, she said, 'Throw the dice and move. You threw two of the same number, so you can throw again.'

The front door shut with a CRASH! and they ran across to the window. Below, the monkeys ran out into the road.

'We must stop them!' said Peter.

'No, we must finish the game, then it will all go away,' said Judy. 'Quickly, throw the dice.'

Peter threw a three and a five. His token moved across the

*They could hear breaking plates and strange screams.*
*Judy pushed open the kitchen door. Inside were twelve*
*brown monkeys. Some threw plates and cups and food across*
*the room. Others threw knives!*

board, and more words came into the glass eye: *This animal is*
*very hungry. Be careful, now! Don't make it angry!*

There was another CRASH! The children turned and saw
something move in a dark corner of the room.

It was a lion! GRRROAARRRR! went the lion.

They screamed and ran downstairs to the next floor, but the
lion jumped down and stood in front of them. They turned
around, ready to run – but now there was a man in front of
them! He had hair over his face, and a very big knife in his
hand. 'Wh – what can we do?' said Peter.

GRRROAARRRR! The lion jumped at them.

11

*GRRROAARRRR! went the lion. They screamed and ran downstairs . . . but the lion jumped down and stood in front of them. They turned around, ready to run.*

They ran past the man. There was a cupboard behind him, and they jumped inside and half-closed the door. They saw the lion coming at the man, but at the last minute he moved and the lion went flying past him – into Aunt Nora's bedroom! The man pulled Aunt Nora's bedroom door shut.

GRRROAARRRR! went the lion. But it could not get out. The man tried to open one of the other doors, but it didn't move. CRASH! He kicked it open with his foot.

Peter and Judy came out of the cupboard carefully and went to the other room. It was a boy's bedroom.

The man was next to an old bike – a boy's bike. Then he opened a cupboard door and looked at the boy's coats and pants inside. Next he saw a photograph on a table by the bed. He looked at it for a long time, then turned to Peter and Judy. 'Did somebody throw a five or an eight?' he asked.

'Yes, me,' said Peter.

The man smiled – then began to laugh. 'Thank you!' he said, then ran out of the room and down the stairs, shouting 'Mom! Dad! Where are you? It's me, Alan! I'm home!'

Peter and Judy ran after him.

'Are you *Alan Parrish*?' Judy asked him.

Alan Parrish, now thirty-eight years old, said, 'Who are you?'

'I'm Judy and he's Peter,' said Judy. 'We live here now. But – everybody thinks you're dead.'

'Where are my mom and dad?' he asked.

'We don't know,' said Judy.

He stopped smiling and turned and ran out through the front door. Peter and Judy followed him into the road.

'Look out!' shouted Judy.

*Screeech!* A new police car stopped suddenly – with Alan on the front of it!

The policeman got out of the car. 'Get down off my car!' he shouted at Alan.

Alan got down and carefully looked at the car. 'What year is it?'

'It's new,' the policeman said. 'I got it today.'

'No, not the car,' said Alan. 'What *year* is it?'

'It's 1995,' said Judy.

Then Alan carefully looked at the name on the policeman's shirt. 'Carl Bentley?' he said.

The policeman turned to Judy. 'Who is he?' he asked.

'He – he's our uncle,' she said quickly. 'From . . . Indonesia.'

Suddenly, Peter saw two monkeys trying to get into Officer

13

Bentley's car. Alan saw them, too, and he made a noise like a lion. The monkeys ran behind the police car.

Officer Bentley turned to Judy. 'Is he OK?' he said.

K-BOOM! Everybody jumped at the noise. Smoke suddenly came out of a hole in the top of Officer Bentley's new car. Two of the monkeys were inside and one of them had the policeman's gun!

The other monkey started the car. *Screeech!* It moved away fast. 'Stop!' shouted Officer Bentley, and ran after it.

Alan began to walk away.

'Wait!' said Judy. 'Where are you going?'

'I'm going to find my Mom and dad,' answered Alan.

'But what about the game?' she asked. 'We must finish it.'

'You finish it,' Alan shouted back at them.

## Chapter 4   Four to Play

Alan walked through the town to an old factory. Outside it said PARRISH SHOES – THE BEST SHOES IN NEW ENGLAND! Peter and Judy followed him into the building. The windows were broken, and there were a lot of old machines round the room. 'Where is everybody?' said Alan. 'My dad made shoes here. The best shoes in New England.'

Suddenly, he saw a man by a door at the top of some stairs. Alan ran up the stairs, and Peter and Judy went after him. The old man had a bed in the center of a room, with a chair and some food next to it.

'He lives here,' thought Peter. 'He lives in this old factory.'

The old man was surprised to see them.

'I'm sorry,' said Alan. 'I thought you were . . . What happened to the shoe factory, do you know?'

'It closed,' said the old man.

'What about the Parrish family?' asked Alan.

'Their son ran away,' said the old man. 'They tried everything to find him. Sam didn't come to work. He didn't want to think about the business. He wanted to find his son.'

'Are Mr and Mrs Parrish in Brantford now?' asked Alan.

'They're dead,' said the old man.

Nobody spoke for a minute, then Alan went out of the room and out of the building. Peter and Judy followed him.

'Our mother and father are dead, too,' said Judy. 'Listen, I know you're unhappy, but can you help my brother and me finish the game?'

'No, sorry,' said Alan. 'I have more important things to do.'

'But there's a lion in my aunt's bedroom!' said Judy.

They followed him back, and up to the little room at the top of the house. He opened one of the big boxes in a corner and took out some trousers and an old shirt.

Judy came up behind him with the game.

'Don't bring that thing near me!' he said. He went downstairs to the bathroom and shut the door.

'But you must help us finish it!' shouted Judy.

He didn't answer. A minute later they heard water running into a bathtub. It was half an hour before he came out again. There was no hair on his face now, and he looked cleaner and much better in a different shirt, coat and pants.

'You could *watch* Peter and I play the game,' said Judy.

They followed him into the kitchen, and he opened the refrigerator. He shouted and moved away quickly when a monkey jumped out. Peter watched this and thought of something.

'Come on, Judy,' he said. 'Alan's too afraid to help us.'

'What!' said Alan. 'I'm *not* afraid! You think monkeys and mosquitoes are bad? I saw much worse things than that in the jungle. That game is too dangerous for children to play!'

'Yes!' said Peter, quickly. '*You* have to play, too. Thanks.'

'All right! All right!' said Alan.

The children smiled, and Judy dropped the dice on to the board. Nothing happened. 'What's wrong?' she said.

'I know!' said Alan. '*I* started that game in 1969! Look, those two tokens are yours, and this one is mine. But there's one more, and *that* token must move next!'

'But who must throw the dice?' said Judy.

'Sarah Whittle,' said Alan, and he walked out of the room.

Judy looked at Peter. 'Here we go again!' she said.

They followed Alan down the street to a house. There were trees around it, and thick vines on the outside. A woman opened the front door. 'What do you want?' she said. She was pretty, but she had a tired face.

Alan looked at her carefully and smiled. 'Sarah!' he said.

'What do you want?' the woman asked again.

'When you were thirteen, you played a game with a boy down the street,' said Alan.

'How do you know *that*?' she asked.

'Because I was the boy,' said Alan.

She looked carefully at him. 'Alan? *Alan!*' Sarah's face went white. Then her eyes closed, and she fell to the floor.


## Chapter 5    Playing the Game

After five minutes, Sarah opened her eyes and sat up.

'You must come back to my house,' said Alan. 'We must show you something. Please, Sarah, it's important.'

*Back in the living room at the Parrish house, they showed
Sarah the game . . . 'Listen,' said Alan. 'Twenty-six years ago
we started something, and now we must all finish it.'*

It took ten more minutes before she said, 'OK, OK!'

Back in the living room at the Parrish house, they showed
Sarah the game. 'Don't bring that thing near me!' she said.

'Listen,' said Alan. 'Twenty-six years ago we started something, and now we must all finish it.' He took her hand and
put the dice into it.

'I – I can't!' she said.

'OK,' said Alan. He put out his hand. 'Give me the dice.'

Sarah gave him the dice – but he moved his hand quickly
and they fell on to the board! Alan smiled. 'Sorry,' he said.

'No, you're not!' said Sarah. 'You wanted –'

*Brummm-tum-tum. Brummm-tum-tum.*

17

Sarah's token moved, and the words came. *Its pretty flower is yellow or blue. But be very careful – it can eat you!*

Peter looked round the room. Vines pushed out from behind pictures, between chairs, through little holes in the floor. They had flowers – yellow and blue. Suddenly, one went round Peter's leg and began to pull him across the room. 'Help!' he shouted. A big yellow flower opened its 'mouth', ready to eat Peter.

Alan got Peter's other leg, and Sarah and Judy took one of his arms. They pulled and pulled but the vine was too strong for them. Alan looked round for something to help them, and he saw a big knife above the fire-place. He took it down.

CRASH! Down came the knife – and cut the vine into two!

Everybody fell back on to the floor, but Peter got his leg away from the vine. Then they all ran into the next room and shut the door behind them.

Sarah wanted to go home.

'The game's not finished,' said Alan.

Judy gave him the dice and he dropped them on to the board. More words. *This man from the jungle has a gun. Go now! Quickly! Run!*

Alan's face went white. 'Van Pelt,' he said.

'Who?' said Judy.

'The hunter, Van Pelt,' said Alan. 'He –'

K-BOOM! CRASH!

First the sound of the gun – then the noise of the door breaking. 'Get down!' screamed Alan, and fell to the floor.

There was a tall man with white hair and a jungle hat and jacket by the broken door. He had a big gun in his hand.

Peter heard a sound and turned round. He saw Alan near the front door of the house. K-BOOM! went the gun again. But Alan got away, and Peter began to run after him.

He ran outside and saw Alan in the street now. A police car stopped outside the house, but Alan ran past it. Officer Bentley jumped out of his car. 'You! Stop!' he shouted.

K-BOOM! Van Pelt's gun went off behind him, and some of the tree above Alan's head crashed down near him.

Officer Bentley turned and shouted at Van Pelt, 'Drop that gun! Put your hands up!'

K-BOOM! K-BOOM! K-BOOM! The hunter answered by breaking the police car's lights and windows. Officer Bentley jumped into his car and – *Screeeech!* – drove away as fast as he could. Then the hunter ran after Alan.

Peter, Judy and Sarah went back into the front room. There were vines with yellow or blue flowers all round the room.

'How can we finish the game now?' said Peter.

'I don't know –' began Judy.

'Who goes next?' said somebody.

Peter and the girls turned and saw Alan climbing in through the window. Alan smiled at Sarah.

Judy laughed. 'I go next,' she said.

Sarah looked angrily at Alan. 'You didn't tell us about that hunter – why? He's trying to kill us!' she said.

'Kill *me*,' said Alan. 'He's trying to kill *me*. He doesn't like me. Why? I don't know.'

'Come on,' Peter said to his sister. 'Throw the dice.'

Judy threw them, and her token moved. More words came into the glass eye: *Look out! It's not the rain that's coming. It's animals – and they're running!*

CRASH! The four of them turned around – *and a big rhinoceros crashed into the room!*

'Quick!' shouted Alan.

They all jumped behind a chair and watched: twenty or more rhinoceroses ran through the living room! Then CRASH! again

*Six big white pelicans flew through the room. The last pelican flew over the Jumanji board, then came back. 'No!' said Alan. But he was too late. The bird had the board-game in its mouth.*

and the animals ran out of the house and across the garden. Next came elephants – and then zebras!

But a minute later, everything was quiet.

'They're going,' said Judy. 'But look, everything is broken!' She was right. Tables, chairs, lights – everything.

Suddenly, six big white pelicans flew through the room. The last pelican flew over the Jumanji board, then came back. 'No!' said Alan. But he was too late. The bird had the board-game in its mouth. 'Peter!' shouted Alan. 'Stop him!'

Peter looked at the big bird – and put his hands over his head. The bird flew over him and out of the house.

'Sorry,' said Peter. 'I–I was afraid.'

Alan was angry. He ran after the pelican.

'Where's he going?' said Judy.

'Water,' said Peter. 'Pelicans like water. Right?'

## Chapter 6   Things Get Worse

They found Alan near Brantford River. He was behind a tree.

'Be quiet!' Alan told them. 'Get down!'

They got down behind the tree. The pelican was on a big dead tree in the water. The game was by its feet.

Alan moved slowly and quietly across to the bird. It turned and looked angrily at him. 'It's all right, friend,' said Alan, and put his hand out to the board. 'You've got my game –'

The bird's answer was to bite Alan's hand.

'Yeowww!' shouted Alan. Then he put a hand in the water – and pulled out a fish! 'Here, birdy!' he called.

The pelican took the fish, and Alan tried to get the game from the tree. But it fell into the river! Peter saw it moving quickly in the water, and ran along next to it. But then it went out into the centre of the river. 'What can I do?' he thought.

Then he saw another tree that was half-across the water. He climbed up on to it, and out over the river. He tried to get his hand in the water. The Jumanji game was under him – but he couldn't get it! He moved up and down on the tree. One, two, three! Up and down went the tree. Now his hand was in the water, and . . . 'Got it!' he shouted.

Judy and Sarah smiled when he climbed back with the game. 'Peter, that was very clever,' said Judy.

'Thanks,' he said. He wanted Alan to say something nice, but Alan didn't look at him.

They walked quickly back to the road.

*Screeech!* Officer Bentley's police car stopped next to them, and he jumped out. 'You!' he shouted at Alan. 'I'm taking you to the police station – I want to ask you some questions.'

'I'm not going,' said Alan.

'Yes, you are,' said Officer Bentley, and he put some handcuffs on Alan and began to pull him over to the car.

'Wait a minute, officer!' said Sarah.

But suddenly it was Alan trying to get Officer Bentley into the car. 'Come on!' he shouted. 'Van Pelt's going to kill me!'

'You children go home,' said Officer Bentley.

'Wait!' said Sarah. 'Don't take him!'

'What's wrong with everybody?' thought Peter. 'We have to finish this game!' His token was only twelve squares from the finish. He took the dice in his fingers. Each dice showed a six. 'All I have to do is drop them carefully to "throw" twelve,' he thought. 'Then my token will finish the game!'

The police car drove away with Alan inside it.

Peter dropped the dice . . . *and his token went back to the beginning of the game!* 'Judy!' he called.

She saw the open board. 'What happened?' she said.

'I – I tried to finish the game with two sixes,' he began.

Words came into the glass eye: *You cheated! That was wrong to do. Now everybody can laugh at you!*

Sarah came over. 'You tried to *cheat*?' she said to Peter.

'Peter!' his sister said suddenly. 'Look at your hands!'

Peter looked down at his hands. There was thick, dark hair on the backs of them!

22

## Chapter 7   More and More Animals

'We must get Alan out of the police station,' said Judy.

They walked back to the town. Peter carried the Jumanji game. Every time he looked at his hands, there was more hair on them. 'Am I turning into a monkey?' he thought.

They stopped at the top of the street. 'Wh – what's happening here?' said Sarah. There were broken cars all down the street. People and monkeys ran in and out of shops. A man went past them on his bike with three monkeys on his back. He had a big mosquito bite on his face.

Suddenly, Judy turned and screamed. Van Pelt was behind them with his gun! 'Give me that,' said the hunter, and took the game from Peter's hairy hands. 'Do you want it back? Then tell Parrish to meet me at –'

'Help!' 'Look out!' 'Run!'

People ran down the street. They screamed and shouted.

Van Pelt looked round – and Peter pulled the game away from him and ran into the street. *Screeech!* A car stopped two feet away from Peter. A man with a red face jumped out, ready to shout. But hundreds of animals started to run down the street! Rhinoceroses, elephants, zebras.

The man ran away and Peter jumped into the car – and an elephant ran over the top of it! 'It's going to kill me!' he thought, and got down on to the car floor. The windows broke, and the top crashed down nearer and nearer to his head. But the elephant and the other animals went past and Peter wasn't dead. But he could not get out of the car.

Van Pelt put his hand inside. Peter thought that the hunter wanted to help him – but he was wrong. The hunter wanted the game. 'Give me that!' he said, and pulled the game out of

*Hundreds of animals started to run down the street!*
*Rhinoceroses, elephants, zebras . . . Peter jumped into the car –*
*and an elephant ran over the top of it!*

Peter's hands. He looked round and then he ran away down the street.

'Help!' shouted Peter. 'Get me out of here!'

Sarah and Judy ran across and pulled Peter out of the car.

'We must get that game back,' said Sarah, and she began to run after Van Pelt.

The hunter went into a supermarket. People ran out past with TVs, radios and other things in their hands.

Sarah, Judy and Peter went inside. 'Look!' shouted Judy.

The Jumanji board was on a table about ten feet away from them. Where was Van Pelt? They couldn't see him.

'Wait here,' said Sarah. She walked to the table and put out

*'Give me that!' Van Pelt said, and pulled the game out of Peter's hands. He looked round and then he ran away down the street.*

a hand to get the game. Van Pelt's fingers went around her arm, and the hunter got up from behind the table.

'Now we wait for Alan to come and get you,' he said.

Sarah tried to get away, but Van Pelt was too strong. 'OK,' she said. 'How is Alan going to know that you've got me?'

K-BOOM! K-BOOM! went Van Pelt's gun. People screamed and ran out through the doors. 'Now he's going to hear about you very soon,' said Van Pelt, and he smiled.

He didn't see Peter and Judy. They were near the table. Peter was now more monkey than boy. Suddenly, he jumped at Van Pelt and bit the hunter's leg with his monkey teeth.

'Yeowww!' shouted Van Pelt, and Sarah ran away from him with the game. Peter and Judy ran, too.

Peter got to the street doors, but the hunter was there before him with the gun in his hand.

'Where is she, monkey-boy?' asked Van Pelt.

'Over there!' said Peter. And when the hunter looked to the right, Peter ran to the left.

K-BOOM! K-BOOM! He heard Van Pelt's gun.

Suddenly, there was a big CRASH! and Alan drove Officer Bentley's police car through the shop's front window. It crashed through TVs, cups, plates, shoes, vegetables, bread – and then into some big cans of fruit. The small mountain of cans crashed down and buried Van Pelt under it!

Alan jumped out of the car. He saw Sarah and Judy.

'You're all right!' he said. 'Where's Peter?'

Peter came out from behind six broken TVs. 'I'm here.'

Alan looked at him. 'You're all . . . monkey!' he said.

'He tried to finish the game by cheating,' Sarah told him.

'Well, we have the game again now,' said Alan. 'We must get back to the house and finish it.'

Officer Bentley climbed out of his car. He had the handcuffs on now, not Alan. And the handcuffs were round the broken car door.

'Do you want me to help you?' asked Alan.

'No!' shouted the policeman, and ran away as fast as he could with the car door behind him.

They walked home, and Alan told them about Carl Bentley.

'He worked at Parrish Shoes when I was a boy,' said Alan, 'and he made America's very first sports shoe. But I put it down on a machine, accidentally. It broke the machine and Carl lost his job. Then he got a job as a policeman.'

'What about the handcuffs?' asked Peter.

'I asked Carl to take them off me, and I quickly put them on him before he could stop me,' said Alan.

'Why?' asked Judy.

'I must finish the game, and I don't want Carl to stop me,' said Alan. 'We heard on the police radio that Van Pelt had Sarah, so I pushed Carl into the car and drove down here.'

'And you crashed through the window, and all those cans of fruit fell on top of Van Pelt,' laughed Judy.

'That was luck,' said Alan. 'I couldn't stop the car.'

They were back at the Parrish house now, and Alan pushed open the door. There were vines all over the room, and over the big glass light above the centre of the room.

Alan put the dice in Sarah's hand. For the first time that day, she gave him a friendly smile. He smiled back.

'Throw a twelve and you can win,' said Judy. 'Sarah?'

'What?' said Sarah. She looked away from Alan. 'OK.'

She shut her eyes and threw the dice. They showed . . . five. There were more words: *It's much too late to run away. The water is coming here today!* 'Water?' said Sarah.

And rain started to fall – inside the house!

Soon, the floor was under water. The Jumanji game started to move away but Alan caught it. Now the water was half up their legs. 'We must get up to a higher place!' shouted Alan.

They went across to the stairs. But water came down fast, and pushed them back. They began to swim. Alan looked up at the glass light in the center of the room. 'Come on!' he shouted, and started to swim across to it.

'*Alan!*' Sarah screamed.

They turned and saw two big crocodiles in the water.

A table moved out of the next room on the water.

*It was a fight between two big man-eating crocodiles
and one man!*

Alan climbed up on to it, then pulled the others up with
him.

'Where are the crocodiles?' said Sarah. Suddenly a crocodile
jumped up, and she screamed.

'Climb!' shouted Alan. And he helped Judy and Peter to
climb up on to the big glass light. One of the crocodiles got
up on the table. At the same time, Peter fell into the water.

'Help!' he shouted. Alan pulled him back.

But now the crocodile on the table had its mouth open.

'Help me!' screamed Sarah. 'I'm falling!'

Alan jumped – and he and the crocodile went under the
water. Now the other crocodile moved across. It was a fight
between two big man-eating crocodiles and one man!

'*Alan!*' screamed Sarah.

## Chapter 8  Down and Down

Suddenly, the water began to go down.

'Somebody opened the front door!' shouted Judy. 'The water is going out.'

Peter put out a hand and caught Alan. The two young women pulled him on to the glass light with them. The four of them waited for the water to go out of the front door, then Peter and Judy jumped down on to the table.

Alan helped Sarah down. 'Alan, you fought a crocodile

*They pulled Alan onto the glass light with them. The four of them waited for the water to go out of the front door.*

for me!' she said, and looked at him with love in her eyes.

'I – well – we must get upstairs,' Alan said quickly.

They went up to the room at the top of the house. Alan put the game down and threw the dice. His token moved to the next square. New words came into the glass eye. *Be careful when you stand or sit. Look! The floor! You're falling through it!* And – slowly, slowly – Alan *did* start to fall through the floor! His feet first, then his legs. The floor was like butter – with Alan falling into it! Down . . . down . . .

'Help me!' he shouted.

His head was above the floor, but that was all! Sarah pushed her arms into the floor, but she couldn't help him.

Judy quickly threw the dice. 'Perhaps this will help,' she thought. But her token didn't move to the next square – it moved back! *There is something you must know,* said the words. *Sometimes it's back that you must go.*

And Alan stopped falling through the floor!

But he couldn't move. Sarah's arms were in the floor, and *she* couldn't move.

'Thanks, Judy,' said Alan. 'That was quick thinking. But Peter must throw the dice next.'

Peter threw them. His token moved, and new words came into the glass eye. *Want a hand? Well, you wait! We can help you – we have eight.*

They heard the sound of hundreds of feet. Then a spider as big as a cat dropped down near them! Sarah and Judy screamed. Peter looked in the dark corners of the room – and saw the red eyes of twenty or thirty big spiders!

'Judy, bring the game, quick!' shouted Alan.

She carried the board over to Alan and Sarah.

'Give me the dice,' said Sarah. 'In my mouth.'

Judy put the dice into Sarah's mouth, and then she opened

*Alan couldn't move. Sarah's arms were in the floor,*
*and she couldn't move . . . Peter threw the dice.*
'Want a hand? Well, you wait! We can help you –
we have eight!'

it. The dice fell on to the board. Her token moved, and there
were new words to read. *Listen to the noise it's making. An animal?*
*No, the house is breaking!* Suddenly the floor began to move! It
broke open and Sarah pulled her hands out of it.

'I'm falling!' shouted Alan.

Sarah's hands went around his arm. 'Got you!'

'The game!' shouted Alan. 'It's going to fall down the hole
in the floor! Get the game!'

But it was too late. The Jumanji board fell down into the
hole and on to the next floor below. Under that was another
bigger, darker hole. And what was below that? Alan didn't want

to think about it. He pushed out a hand and put his fingers round a vine, climbed down it and got the Jumanji board. Then he stood on the floor of the front room.

He put the game board down and took the dice in his hand. 'I'm going to finish this game!' he said. 'I must!'

'Don't move!' said somebody behind him.

Alan went cold all over. Van Pelt was behind him with his gun. 'What's that in your hand?' asked Van Pelt. 'Drop it!'

'Do it, Alan,' said Sarah, and she came down the stairs. Only half the stairs were there now.

Alan dropped the dice. One fell on to the board. It showed a three. The other fell off – *and down the hole!*

'Now we can *never* finish the game!' Alan thought.

'Playing with games?' said Van Pelt. 'Well, now you can run. I'm going to count to three. One . . .' Alan didn't move.

'Two . . .' Van Pelt looked along his gun at Alan. Alan looked back at him. 'Three!' Alan did not move.

'So you're not afraid?' said Van Pelt. 'Any last words?'

Alan looked down at the Jumanji board – *and saw that his token was at the finish! He was the winner!*

'Er – Jumanji?' he said, weakly.

K-BOOM!


## Chapter 9   1969 Again

'No!' screamed Sarah, and jumped in front of Alan. She put her arms round him, and he put his arms round her. Suddenly they were going round . . . and round . . . Van Pelt wasn't there now! And everything from the world of Jumanji – the vines,

*'No!' screamed Sarah, and jumped in front of Alan.*

the mosquitoes, the spiders, monkeys, rhinoceroses, elephants, zebras, *everything* – went *shuummmppp!* – back into the game board!

Alan looked at Sarah. She looked at him. They were different. Sarah was thirteen again! He was twelve!

*It was 1969!*

They heard the front door open and Sam Parrish came in.

'Dad!' said Alan. 'You're back.'

'I forgot something,' said Sam Parrish.

Alan ran across the room and threw his arms around his father. 'Dad! Dad!' he said happily. 'I'm sorry.'

Sam looked surprised, but he smiled. 'I was angry, Alan, but I'm sorry, too,' he said. 'And about Cliffside –'

'Cliffside?' said Alan. What was Cliffside? He couldn't

remember. 'Dad, today, in the factory, you remember the machine that broke? Carl didn't do it. I accidentally put that shoe on the machine.'

Sam Parrish looked at his son and said, 'Thank you for telling me that, son.' Then he turned and went out.

Alan smiled at Sarah. Then he looked at the game board. 'Judy! Peter!' he said quickly. 'We must go up to –'

'They're not *born*,' said Sarah. 'We're back in 1969.' She opened her hand. Judy's and Peter's tokens were in it.

'You're right,' said Alan, sadly. 'But there is something we must do. Come on.'

They put the Jumanji game into a big box, then went down to the Brantford River. They found something heavy to put inside the box, then Alan dropped it into the river. They watched it go slowly down . . . down . . . under the water.

'We mustn't *forget* Peter and Judy,' said Sarah.

'No,' said Alan. 'We mustn't.'

He looked into her eyes, and she looked into his.

'There's something I want to do,' said Sarah.

And she moved nearer to him.


## Chapter 10   1995

It was a winter's day. Alan Parrish was thirty-eight years old. He and another man walked through the Parrish Shoe factory.

The man said, 'The shops are angry with you, Mr Parrish. You're giving away shoes again this Christmas, right?'

'I'm going to give them to children, Marty,' said Alan, and he smiled. 'They aren't going to go out and pay ninety dollars for sports shoes – we know that. So the shops aren't going to lose any money, you see?'

'But we are,' said Marty.

'These people are not always going to be children,' said Alan. 'And when they get jobs, they're going to remember Parrish Shoes, and they're going to buy them.'

They went past an office and Carl Bentley came out. He was forty-six years old, and an important man in the factory now. He smiled at Alan, then said, 'Come into my office, Marty, and we can talk about it.'

That night, Alan talked to his father on the phone in the kitchen of his house. Sam Parrish and his wife lived in Florida now. '1995 was another good year, Dad,' said Alan.

The kitchen door opened and Sarah came in.

'They're here Alan,' she said.

'Dad, I must go,' Alan said into the phone. 'Give my love to Mom.' He followed Sarah out of the kitchen. He had a shoe box in each hand. Each box had Christmas paper round it.

There were a lot of people in the next room, and children stood and looked at a big Christmas tree in the corner.

Alan spoke to a man about thirty-five years old. The man's wife was with him. 'I'm happy you could come tonight,' said Alan.

'Thanks,' said Jim Shepherd. 'This is my wife, Martha.' He looked round. 'Where are the children, Martha?'

A twelve-year-old girl and an eight-year-old boy pushed their way through the people. 'Here they are,' said Alan.

'How did you know them?' asked Martha.

'I –' Alan began, then stopped.

'Well, you're right,' said Jim. 'This is Judy . . . and Peter. Children, meet Mr and Mrs Parrish.'

'Hello,' said Peter.

'Nice to meet you,' said Judy.

*'Thank you,' said Judy. She read the name on them.
'Jumanjis! What a strange name.' Alan and Sarah smiled
and said nothing.*

Alan gave the shoe boxes to them. 'Happy Christmas!' he
said. He and Sarah were very happy to see them again.

'Martha and I are thinking about going to Canada, for a
holiday,' said Jim Shepherd. 'We –'

'*No!*' Alan and Sarah said together.

Jim and Martha Shepherd were surprised.

'Er – sorry,' Alan said to Jim. 'But we – we –'

'We want you to start work on the new shoes at the factory
as soon as you can,' Sarah finished for him.

Jim looked at his wife. 'OK. We can always have a holiday
another time. I can start next week.'

Peter and Judy opened the shoe boxes. They each pulled out some new sports shoes.

'Thanks, Mr Parrish!' said Peter, with a big smile.

'Do you like them?' said Alan.

'Yes, thank you,' said Judy. She read the name on them. 'Jumanjis! What a strange name.'

Alan looked at Sarah, and she looked at him.

They smiled and said nothing.

# ACTIVITIES

## Chapters 1–3

*Before you read*

1   Look at the picture on the front of this book. What do you think Jumanji is?

2   Find these words in your dictionary. Do you understand all of them?
    *bury  crash  glass  refrigerator  scream*
    Now answer the questions:
    **a**   Which two words tell you about sounds?
    **b**   Which word means, 'to put something in the ground'?
    **c**   Which word is used for windows and bottles?
    **d**   Which word is a cold place for food?

3   Finish these sentences:
    *bite  drop  hole  machine  surprised*
    **a**   Be careful! That dog will ..... you with its teeth!
    **b**   You use a washing ..... to wash your jeans and jackets.
    **c**   There's a ..... in this shoe and when it rains my foot gets wet.
    **d**   She ..... the cup and it broke.
    **e**   John told me he got married last week and I was very ......

*After you read*

4   Why doesn't Alan tell his father he put Carl's sports shoe on the machine?

5   How does Alan find Jumanji?

6   Why does Sarah come to Alan's house?

7   What happens when Alan throws a two and a three with the dice?

8   What does Aunt Nora want to do with the house in Brantford?

9   How does Alan get back to the house?

10   What happens to Officer Bentley's car?

## Chapters 4–7

*Before you read*

11  Look up these words in your dictionary:
    *broken  cheat*
    Now write a sentence with each word to show that you under-
    stand them.
12  Where do you think Alan will go to look for his parents?
13  Do you think Peter and Judy can finish the game without Alan?
    Why or why not?

*After you read*

14  Who asks these questions? Who to?
    a  'What happened to the shoe factory, do you know?'
    b  'How do you know *that*?'
    c  'How can we finish the game now?'
    d  'How is Alan going to know that you've got me?'
15  Which animals run through the house?
16  How do they lose the Jumanji board?
17  Who gets the Jumanji board back?
18  What does Peter try to do with his dice? Why?
19  How does Alan stop Van Pelt?
20  Which animals come into the house with the water?

## Chapters 8–10

*Before you read*

21  What do you think will happen next?
22  Do you think somebody will come to help them? Who?
23  What do you think will happen when the game finishes?
24  Which year do you think the story finishes in?

*After you read*

25  Where do these things happen?

    **a**   Alan starts to fall through the floor.

    **b**   Van Pelt comes up behind Alan with a gun.

    **c**   Alan and Sarah put something heavy into a box with the Jumanji game.

**26**  Who ...

    **a**   ... pulls Alan on to the glass light?

    **b**   ... puts the dice in Sarah's mouth?

    **c**   ... wins the game?

    **d**   ... changes their holiday plans?

**27**  Where does Carl Bentley work in 1995?

**28**  Where do Sam Parrish and his wife live in 1995?

**29**  Why don't Alan and Sarah want Jim Shepherd and his wife to go to Canada for a holiday?

**30**  What does Alan give Peter and Judy for Christmas?


**Writing**

**31**  Look at the photographs from the film. Now write two or three sentences about three of them. What is happening? Who is in the photograph? What do they look like? How do they feel?

**32**  Would you like to take a journey through time? Would you like to go to the future or the past? Which year would you like to go to and why?

**33**  Which part of the story did you find most exciting? Why? Write about it.

**34**  Finish these sentences:

    **a**   Peter quickly put the photograph of his mum and dad away before his sister came into his bedroom because .....

    **b**   Sarah didn't want to play Jumanji again because .....

    **c**   Alan Parrish gave sports shoes to children at Christmas because ....